STEPPING STONES

A Path to Critical Thinking

········· **Book 2** ·············

Vera Schneider

Illustrated by Ruth Linstromberg

Educators Publishing Service, Inc.
Cambridge and Toronto

Dr. Frederick J. Stokley, Superintendent of Schools in Ridgewood, New Jersey, initiated the idea of publishing Ridgewood curriculum. He hoped that Ridgewood could contribute to American education by sharing material that has proved particularly stimulating and effective in Ridgewood schools.

Curriculum developed by Vera Schneider at Ridgewood Public Schools, Ridgewood, New Jersey

Educators Publishing Service, Inc.
31 Smith Place
Cambridge, MA 02138-1089
1-800-225-5750
www.epsbooks.com

Design by Persis Barron Levy and Karen Lomigora

To Jim, Kevin, and Mary,
To my mother,
and
In memory of my father.

With sincere appreciation and gratitude to

- my husband, Jim, for his love and patience and whose help made the completion of this book possible

- my children, Kevin and Mary, who are my motivation and who, I hope, will always set goals for themselves and work hard to achieve them

- my mother, for her strength, for her prayers, and for believing in me

- Stephanie Zaccaria, whose advice I constantly seek, whose expertise I greatly respect, and whose friendship I cherish, for always taking the time to be there for me

- Louise Mullin, who brings joy and laughter into my world, who helps me keep things in proper perspective, and who is a great and treasured source of support and friendship

- my students, past and present, who amaze me with their wonderful thoughts and ideas, their awe of the world, and their delight for learning

- my relatives, friends, and colleagues, who encourage me each step of the way

- Dr. Sharon Piety-Jacobs, who taught me to think about thinking

Contents

WARM-UP EXERCISES

Cross out the item that does not belong in each set.
How did you make your choice?

1   bee   bear   ant   bat

2   ice skate   snowman   beach ball   sled

3   wind   rain   snow   lamp

Cross out the item that does not belong in each set.
How did you make your choice?

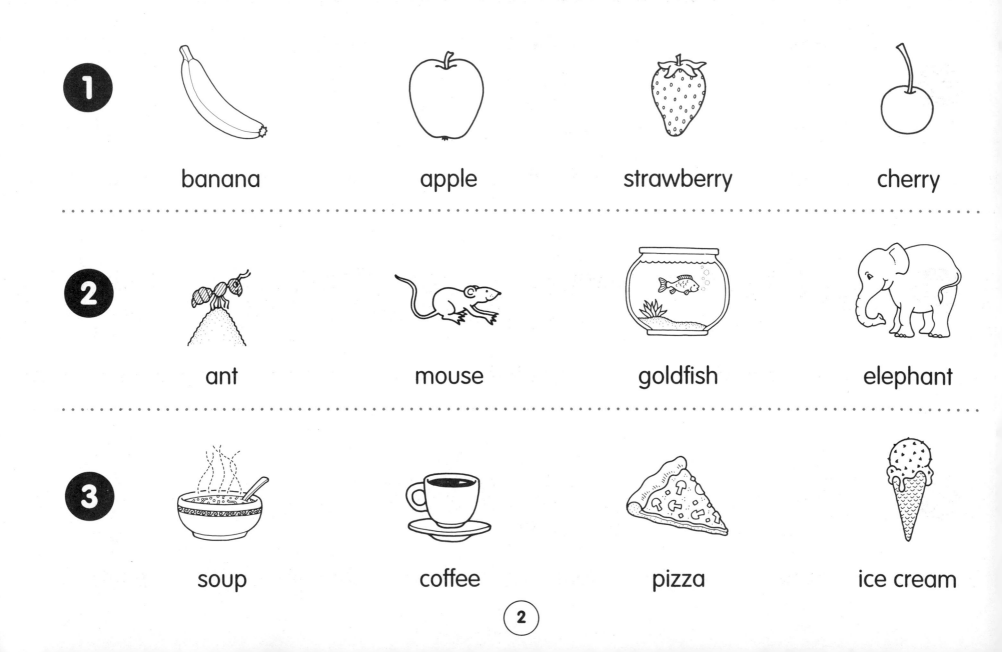

1
banana   apple   strawberry   cherry

2
ant   mouse   goldfish   elephant

3
soup   coffee   pizza   ice cream

Name _____ **Date** _____

Cross out the item that does not belong in each set.
How did you make your choice?

1
two   seven   five   star

2
ham   bell   well   tell

3
hand   foot   ear   pants

Cross out the item that does not belong in each set.
How did you make your choice?

1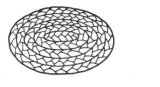

rug   hat   egg   flower

2

dog   cat   fish   pig

3

carrot   corn   broccoli   cucumber

Cross out the item that does not belong in each set. How did you make your choice?

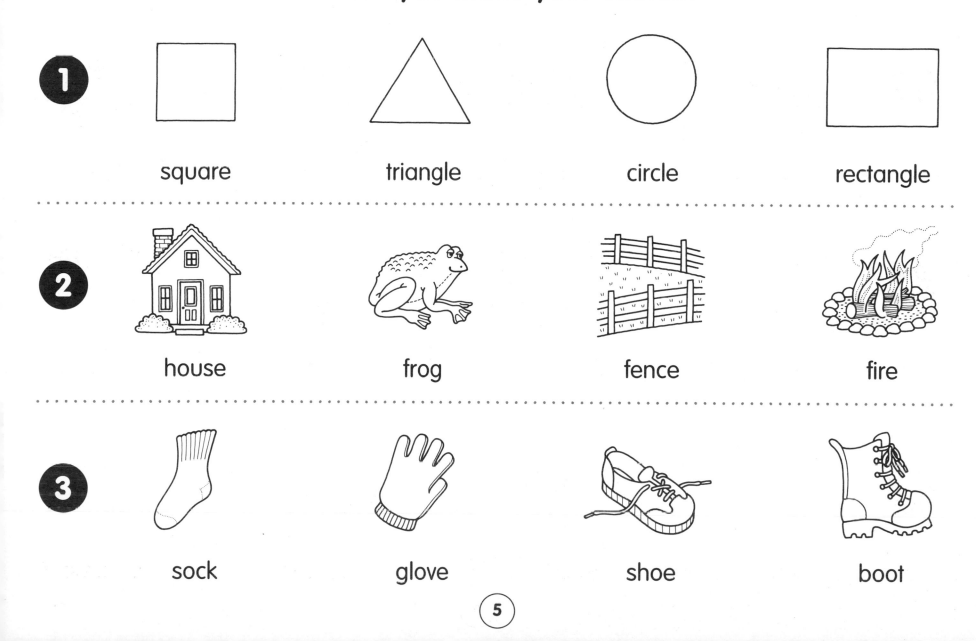

1
square   triangle   circle   rectangle

2
house   frog   fence   fire

3
sock   glove   shoe   boot

Cross out the item that does not belong in each set.
How did you make your choice?

1

car   bike   wagon   chair

2

turkey   tomato   top   hamburger

3

grapes   marbles   cards   doll

Cross out the item that does not belong in each set.
How did you make your choice?

 1

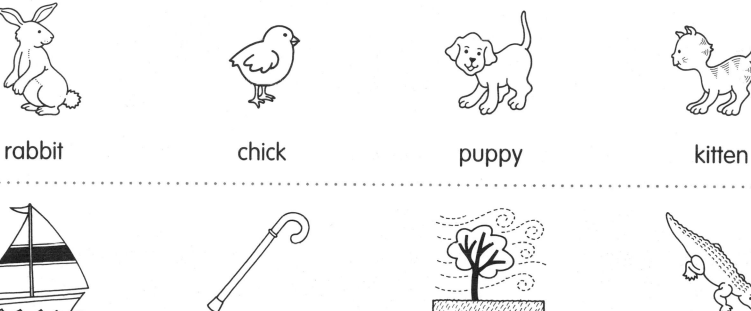

rabbit   chick   puppy   kitten

2

boat   cane   wind   alligator

  **3**

butterfly   bird   airplane   bus

Cross out the set that does not belong with the others.
How did you make your choice?

ant

rabbit

seal

duck

bear

snake

dog

elephant

cat

turtle

tiger

frog

SENTENCE
COMPLETIONS

Circle an answer or draw one of your own. Think about the pictures and the words carefully before you choose your answer.

Jessica was very tired.

She put on her nightgown and went to _____.

sleep

swim

play

paint

_____

Circle an answer or draw one of your own. Think about the pictures and the words carefully before you choose your answer.

Steven had a fever and a sore throat.

He called a _____.

clown   football player   doctor   ballerina   _____

Circle an answer or draw one of your own. Think about the pictures and the words carefully before you choose your answer.

Sam realized that he was lost.

He knew that he needed to find a _____.

map

watch

TV

beach ball   _____

Circle an answer or draw one of your own. Think about the pictures and the words carefully before you choose your answer.

As Nikki was leaving for work, a button fell off of her blouse.

She needed a _____.

hammer

needle and
thread

lamp

ice skate

_____

Circle an answer or draw one of your own. Think about the pictures and the words carefully before you choose your answer.

Ben was hungry.

He wanted a _____.

car

dog

sandwich

chair

_____

Circle an answer or draw one of your own. Think about the pictures and the words carefully before you choose your answer.

Jonathan wanted a book to read.

He went to the _____.

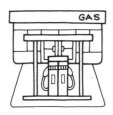

gas station

ocean

food store

library

_____

Circle an answer or draw one of your own. Think about the pictures and the words carefully before you choose your answer.

The Ducans went out to dinner.

Father had fish.

Mom had macaroni.

Helen had a hamburger.

Susan had _____.

pizza   soup   cake   eggs   _____

Circle an answer or draw one of your own. Think about the pictures and the words carefully before you choose your answer.

Lia wore a hat.

Paul wore a coat.

Delia wore pants.

Andrea wore a _____.

wig

ring

dress   blouse   _____

Circle an answer or draw one of your own. Think about the pictures and the words carefully before you choose your answer.

There were three balls under the tree.

There were five balls under the fence.

There were _____ balls under the steps.

six balls   one ball   four balls   two balls   _____

Circle an answer or draw one of your own. Think about the pictures and the words carefully before you choose your answer.

Kevin put bananas on his cereal.

He put onions on his pizza.

He put rice in his soup.

He put salt on his _____.

tomato

apple

grapes

popcorn

_____

Name _____   Date _____

Circle an answer or draw one of your own. Think about the pictures and the words carefully before you choose your answer.

Jim is an artist.

On Sunday, he painted a picture of a bird.

On Monday, he painted a picture of a dog.

On Tuesday, he painted a picture of a pony.

On Wednesday, Jim painted a picture of a _____.

snake

cat

rabbit

dinosaur

_____

Circle an answer or draw one of your own. Think about the pictures and the words carefully before you choose your answer.

David likes dogs.

Trevor likes tigers.

Hana likes horses.

Ben likes _____.

rabbits

turtles

horses

bears

_____

Name _____   Date _____

**Circle an answer or draw one of your own. Think about the
pictures and the words carefully before you choose your answer.**

Stella put sweaters, hats, gloves, and a scarf into the trunk.

Then she put in _____.

mittens

glasses

books

socks _____

Circle an answer or draw one of your own. Think about the pictures and the words carefully before you choose your answer.

Violet lives in Virginia.

Tam lives in Texas.

Rob lives in Rhode Island.

Nancy lives in _____.

New Mexico   Florida   California   Texas   _____

INFERENCE
STATEMENTS

Color the happy face if the last sentence is probably true.
Color the sad face if the last sentence is probably false.

Basketball players are very tall.

Anna is very tall.

Anna must be a basketball player.

All living things need water.

Plants are living.

Plants need water.

All frogs can hop.

Freddie is a frog.

Freddie can hop.

Color the happy face if the last sentence is probably true.
Color the sad face if the last sentence is probably false.

1 It is Dakota's birthday.

Dad is busy baking something in the oven.

Dad must be making a cake for Dakota.

2 Amber got an envelope.

Then Amber looked for a stamp.

Amber wanted to mail a letter.

3 Clowns are funny.

Jon is funny.

Jon must be a clown.

Color the happy face if the last sentence is probably true.
Color the sad face if the last sentence is probably false.

1 Matthew is Maria's son.

Matthew is in kindergarten.

Maria is Matthew's mother.

2 Babies cry when they are hungry.

Baby John is crying.

Baby John must be hungry.

3 Cars have wheels.

A wagon has wheels.

A wagon must be a type of car.

Color the happy face if the last sentence is probably true.
Color the sad face if the last sentence is probably false.

 Kristen likes all flowers.

Kristen does not like weeds.

Kristen likes roses.

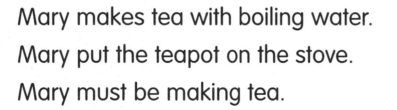 Mary makes tea with boiling water.

Mary put the teapot on the stove.

Mary must be making tea.

 Sabrina loves to eat peanut butter with jelly.

Sabrina loves to eat sandwiches.

Sabrina loves to eat peanut butter and jelly sandwiches.

Color the happy face if the last sentence is probably true.
Color the sad face if the last sentence is probably false.

1   All houses have a roof.

I live in a house.

It must have a roof.

2   All houses have a roof.

My home has a roof.

My home must be a house.

3   You use your nose to smell.

Shane smells cookies baking.

Shane is using his nose.

Color the happy face if the last sentence is probably true.
Color the sad face if the last sentence is probably false.

1 The flag was waving.

The leaves on the tree were rustling.

Suki was putting her kite together.

It was a windy day.

2 Horses have tails.

Tate has a tail.

Tate must be a horse.

3 Bananas are yellow.

The sun is yellow.

The sun is a banana.

Color the happy face if the last sentence is probably true.
Color the sad face if the last sentence is probably false.

1
All apples are fruits.
I have an apple.
It must be a fruit.

2
All bears have fur.
Lucky is a bear.
Lucky must have fur.

3
Water is clear.
My window is clear.
My window must be made out of water.

Color the happy face if the last sentence is probably true.
Color the sad face if the last sentence is probably false.

1

All living things grow.

A tree is a living thing.

A tree must grow.

2

If you know the names of all of the people in a family,

then you can figure out how many people are in the family.

3

If you know how many people are in a family,

then you can figure out all of their names.

Color the happy face if the last sentence is probably true.
Color the sad face if the last sentence is probably false.

 All planets are round.

A basketball is round.

A basketball is a planet.

 All planets are round.

The moon is round.

The moon must be a planet.

 All planets are round.

Jupiter is a planet.

Jupiter must be round.

Color the happy face if the last sentence is probably true.
Color the sad face if the last sentence is probably false.

 Kyle gets up early on school days.

Kyle is sleeping late today.

Kyle is not going to school today.

 Doctors are smart.

Carol is smart.

Carol must be a doctor.

 Dogs are wonderful pets.

Patches is a wonderful pet.

Patches must be a dog.

Color the happy face if the last sentence is probably true.
Color the sad face if the last sentence is probably false.

Pizza has cheese on it.

Jim is eating cheese.

Jim must be eating pizza.

In the alphabet, *G, H, I* comes before *Q, R, S*.

The missing letter comes before *Q, R, S* and it is not *G* or *I*.

The missing letter must be *H*.

Teeth are for chewing food.

Combs have teeth.

Combs must eat.

Color the happy face if the last sentence is probably true.
Color the sad face if the last sentence is probably false.

 Friends like each other.
Alicia likes popcorn.
Popcorn and Alicia are friends.

 All birds have feathers.
Carlos has feathers.
Carlos must be a bird.

 All airplanes have wings.
A parakeet has wings.
A parakeet must be an airplane.

INFERENCE
QUESTIONS

Color the happy face if the answer is *yes*.
Color the sad face if the answer is *no*. Color the
questioning face if there is not enough information to know the answer.

Greg will put a penny, a marble, and a toy car into the bag.
He will not put a ping pong ball or a boat into the bag.
Will Greg put a cork into the bag?

The speed limit was 50 miles per hour.
The policeman gave Sari a ticket.
Was Sari driving faster than the speed limit?

Trucks are not allowed on Pine Street.
Pine Street is the only road to Jamal's mother's house.
Can Jamal drive to visit his mother?

Color the happy face if the answer is *yes*.
Color the sad face if the answer is *no*. Color the
questioning face if there is not enough information to know the answer.

1 Li is bigger than Al.

Max is bigger than Li.

Is Al bigger than Max?

The soup is hotter than the pizza.

2 The coffee is hotter than the soup.

Is the coffee hotter than the pizza?

The pond is deeper than the puddle.

 The lake is deeper than the pond.

Is the puddle deeper than the stream?

Color the happy face if the answer is *yes*.
Color the sad face if the answer is *no*. Color the
questioning face if there is not enough information to know the answer.

 1 Finn's mother named her children in alphabetical order.
Finn's older brother is named Carl.
Could Finn's older sister be named Harriet?

· ·

 2 Winter begins in December.
Summer begins in June.
Is April a summer month?

· ·

3 On weekdays, the light in the office building goes
on at 5:00 in the morning and off at 8:00 at night.
Today is Saturday.
Is the light on?

Color the happy face if the answer is *yes*.
Color the sad face if the answer is *no*. Color the
questioning face if there is not enough information to know the answer.

1 Mary is Christi's friend.

Mary is Alana's friend

Is Christi Alana's friend?

2 Flora is older than Sam.

Sam is younger than Paul.

Is Sam younger than Flora?

3 Mr. Ramirez cannot go home until the children leave.

The children leave at 10:00.

Can Mr. Ramirez go home at 2:00?

Color the happy face if the answer is *yes*.
Color the sad face if the answer is *no*. Color the
questioning face if there is not enough information to know the answer.

The red paint did not show up on the red paper.

The blue paint did not show up on the blue paper.

Did the green paint show up on the green paper?

Jade and Carol are identical twins.

Carol is very tall.

Is Jade tall?

Dentists help people whose teeth hurt.

Rachel's teeth hurt.

Should Rachel go to the dentist?

Color the happy face if the answer is *yes*.
Color the sad face if the answer is *no*. Color the
questioning face if there is not enough information to know the answer.

Jasper always wears sneakers on Tuesdays.

Jasper is not wearing sneakers.

Is it Tuesday?

2

Ball rhymes with *tall.*

Fall rhymes with *ball.*

Does *fall* rhyme with *tall?*

You can see animals that live in water at an aquarium.

Fish live in water.

Can you see fish at an aquarium?

SEQUENCING
ACTIVITIES

Color the happy face if the sentences make sense.
Color the sad face if something is wrong with the sentences.

 Diego called a tow truck and then got a flat tire.

 Peter was in a hurry. He ran upstairs and put on his shoes. Then he looked for his socks.

 Dad put the lawn mower away and then mowed the lawn.

Color the happy face if the sentences make sense.
Color the sad face if something is wrong with the sentences.

1 Grandma closed the umbrella and went out into the rain.

2 Stephanie finished reading and closed the book.

3 Jack dialed the phone number and talked to his uncle.

Color the happy face if the sentences make sense.
Color the sad face if something is wrong with the sentences.

 Sara opened her mouth wide and then sat in the dentist's chair.

Robert put the top back on the toothpaste tube. Then he turned on the water and put the toothpaste on his toothbrush.

 Malik toasted the bread and then spread butter on it.

Color the happy face if the sentences make sense.
Color the sad face if something is wrong with the sentences.

 1 When Rebecca fell and scraped her knee, the school nurse put a bandage on the cut and then put some first aid cream on it.

2 Mitchell put on his bathing suit and went swimming.

 3 Trevor unbuttoned his coat and then went out to play.

Color the happy face if the sentences make sense.
Color the sad face if something is wrong with the sentences.

1 The leaves fell off of the tree, and the wind began to blow.

2 Kate popped popcorn and poured melted butter over it.

3 Samantha bought a pumpkin and rushed home to carve it.

Color the happy face if the sentences make sense.
Color the sad face if something is wrong with the sentences.

 1 Mr. Sato ate the cake and then turned on the oven to bake it.

2 Julia got out of bed, got dressed, and then woke up.

3 William planted the trees and waited for the apples to grow on them.

54

Color the happy face if the sentences make sense.
Color the sad face if something is wrong with the sentences.

1 Molly washed the clothes and then put them in the dryer.

2 The sky grew dark, and it began to rain.

3 Darcy brought groceries home and then put them away.

Color the happy face if the sentences make sense.
Color the sad face if something is wrong with the sentences.

 Ben picked up the phone and it rang.

 Ms. Noon lit the fireplace, and the room got warmer.

 Charlie answered the door and the doorbell rang.

Color the happy face if the sentences make sense.
Color the sad face if something is wrong with the sentences.

1 Bella fell asleep and then set the alarm clock.

2 Ann mailed the package and then put the stamps on it.

3 The speaker finished, and everyone clapped.

Color the happy face if the sentences make sense.
Color the sad face if something is wrong with the sentences.

 1 Cathy drove home and buckled her seatbelt.

 2 Everyone sang "Happy Birthday," and then Aunt Terri lit the candles on the cake.

 3 Lisa put film in the camera and took pictures of her children.

Color the happy face if the sentences make sense.
Color the sad face if something is wrong with the sentences.

1 Cho put the dishes away and then started the dishwasher.

2 The egg hatched, and then the chicken sat on the shell to keep it warm.

3 Michael tied his shoes and then put them on.

Color the happy face if the sentences make sense.
Color the sad face if something is wrong with the sentences.

 1 Chris opened the envelope and then read the letter.

 2 Luis sat on the chair and then moved it to the next table so that he could eat with his friends.

 3 Jean washed her hands and wiped them on a clean towel.

Color the happy face if the sentences make sense.
Color the sad face if something is wrong with the sentences.

1 Helen turned on the radio and then put the batteries in it.

2 Dana closed the box and locked it.

3 Mark wrapped the present and then put it in a box.

61

Color the happy face if the sentences make sense.
Color the sad face if something is wrong with the sentences.

 1 Chen ran to first base and then hit the ball.

 2 Lauren planted the seed and then watered it.

 3 Will felt cold and then put on a sweater.

LOGIC PROBLEMS

Circle the answer that makes the most sense.

Terry is Kevin's parent.

Terry is not Kevin's father.

Who is Terry?

Circle the answer that makes the most sense.

It is very hot in Florida.

Tom does not own any clothes that he could wear in Florida.

What is something you might see where Tom lives?

Circle the answer that makes the most sense.

Jackson and Max wear the same size shoes.

Max wears a size eight.

What size shoe does Jackson wear?

Circle the answer that makes the most sense.

Krista and Pia went in the car to visit the city.

Pia is six years old.

Who drove the car?

Circle the answer that makes the most sense.

The snack bar only sells hot dogs and hamburgers.

Elsie ate at the snack bar.

Elsie hates hamburgers.

What did Elsie eat?

Circle the answer that makes the most sense.

Mike and Paul always do everything the opposite of each other.

When Mike makes a ham and cheese sandwich, he always puts the cheese on top.

What does Paul put on top?

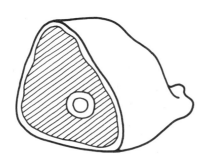 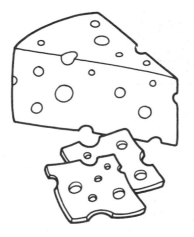  

Circle the answer that makes the most sense.

Kevin is eating pancakes.

Mary is eating scrambled eggs.

What time of day is it?

Circle the answer that makes the most sense.

David can only have a bird or a fish for a pet.

David's pet is not a bird.

What kind of pet does David have?

Circle the answer that makes the most sense.

Dale's dad is older than Dale's mom.

Dale's mom is 37 years old.

How old is Dale's dad?

12   24   42   37

Circle the answer that makes the most sense.

Ramon and Jill entered a big room and sat in the tenth row.

Within minutes, the lights went out.

Ramon and Jill looked up at the big rectangle.

What were Ramon and Jill about to do?

Circle the answer that makes the most sense.

Mom got an old blanket out of the closet.

She filled a big basket with sandwiches, snacks, and drinks.

Where was Mom planning to go?

Circle the answer that makes the most sense.

A big fish saw a little fish and ate the little fish all up.

A big fish saw a little bug and ate the little bug all up.

A big fish saw a little worm and this time the big fish was the one to get all eaten up.

What happened to the big fish?

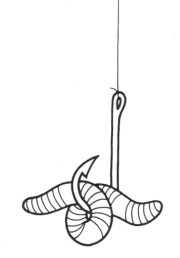

Circle the answer that makes the most sense.

Lane planted a row of flowers around the house.

Lane's row of flowers was in a pattern.

He planted a tulip, a daisy, a tulip, and another daisy.

What did Lane plant next?

Circle the answer that makes the most sense.

Stephen always ate an apple one day and then a pear on the next day.

Stephen ate an apple on Thursday.

What fruit did Stephen eat on the following Tuesday?

Circle the answer that makes the most sense.

Sal always eats a snack after school.

He is allergic to milk products.

What is not a good snack for Sal?

Circle the answer that makes the most sense.

Mother gives Tom his medicine every four hours.

Tom last took his medicine at 11:00.

It is 1:00.

How many more hours does Tom need to wait for his medicine?

Explain why or how. Write or dictate your answer.

There are three tables.

Each table has six chairs.

Seven children want to have lunch together at the same table.

How can they solve this problem?

_____

- -

_____

- -

_____

- -

_____

Explain why or how. Write or dictate your answer.

When Bart was 6 years old, he got 4 new teeth.

When Bart was 4 years old, he had 16 teeth.

When Bart was 7 years old, he had 15 teeth.

Why?

_____

- -

_____

_____

_____

- -

_____

_____

- -

_____

Explain why or how. Write or dictate your answer.

Susan and Sally both watered their gardens for 15 minutes at a time.

Susan watered her garden once a day.

Sally watered her garden at 6:00.

Susan's garden got only half the water that Sally's did.

Why?

_____

- -

_____

_____

- -

_____

_____

- -

_____

Explain why or how. Write or dictate your answer.

Debra's flower wilted in three days.

Paula's flower wilted in five days.

Liv's flower never wilted.

Why?

_____

- -

_____

_____

- -

_____

_____

- -

_____

Explain why or how. Write or dictate your answer.

Mother called the babysitter.

Then she went upstairs to change back into her sweatpants.

Mother was disappointed.

Why?

_____

_____

_____

_____

Explain why or how. Write or dictate your answer.

Carmen wore her favorite dress to school on the first day of every month.

Some years Carmen wore her dress fewer than nine times.

Carmen never wore her dress more than nine times.

Why?

Explain why or how. Write or dictate your answer.

Every time Dan traveled south the weather got colder.

Every time Dan traveled north the weather got colder.

Why?

_____

- -

_____

_____

- -

_____

_____

- -

_____

Explain why or how. Write or dictate your answer.

Stacey has to assign seats around a table for 36 children.

There are 20 boys and 16 girls.

Stacey does not want to have all the boys together or all of the girls together.

She does not want the children to sit in a pattern.

How can Stacey decide where to have the children sit?

_____

- -

_____

- -

_____

- -

_____

- -